1001
THINGS TO FIND

1 GYM BAG

2 SPEAKERS

2 PAIRS OF SHOES

4 SPORTS CUPS

3 STAGE LIGHTS

STAGE SCHOOL

igloobooks

CAN YOU FIND 1001 STAGE SCHOOL THINGS?

Welcome to Superstar Stage School. Lily, Eddie and their friends are warming up for their chance to win the Big Theatre Challenge. Join them as they twirl, leap and sing to wow the judges.

See if you can spot Lily, Eddie and 12 different awards throughout the book, plus lots of other exciting stage school things, too.

Eddie

Lily

12 awards

Let's practise first. On the opposite page, the Pop Singing Round has begun. Can you find Lily, Eddie and the Pop Singing Award? Once you've found them, have a go at spotting these items, too.

6 music sheets

12 headsets

18 water bottles

STREET DANCE

It's time for round two. These awesome street dance crews are getting ready to perform their best routines. Spot Lily, Eddie and the Street Dance Award.

 3 basketballs

 4 crew logos

 5 skateboards

 6 purple headbands

 7 barrels

8 headphones

 9 megaphones

10 gold chains

 12 gloves

 15 baseball caps

THE BIG THEATRE CHALLENGE

DREAM DESIGNS

For round three, the judges want to see the students design a set for a big show. Can you spot Lily, Eddie and the Set Design Award?

3 paint rollers

4 magazines

5 ladders

6 erasers

7 paper balls

8 paint pots

9 jars of glitter

10 glue bottles

12 paintbrushes

15 artist's hats

AWESOME ACTING

In round four, it's time for some serious acting skills. The stage is set and the audience is having fun. Spot Lily, Eddie and the Acting Skills Award.

3 clocks

6 fake moustaches

9 pretty roses

10 apples

15 books

FANTASTIC ACROBATICS

Welcome to round five, where the bendiest dancers are stretching and leaping to win. Can you find Lily, Eddie and the Acrobatic Dance Award?

3 blue balls

7 skipping ropes

8 striped leotards

9 bananas

15 green socks

No show is complete without incredible costumes. The students have been busy creating their designs. Search for Lily, Eddie and the Costume Design Award.

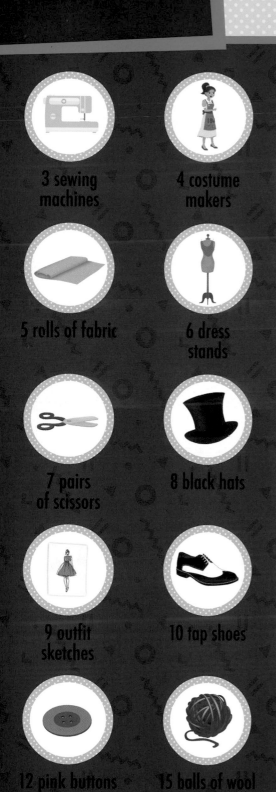

3 sewing machines

4 costume makers

5 rolls of fabric

6 dress stands

7 pairs of scissors

8 black hats

9 outfit sketches

10 tap shoes

12 pink buttons

15 balls of wool

THE **BIG**
THEATRE CHALLENGE

DAZZLING DANCERS

Round seven is the students' chance to show off their perfect technique in ballet and tap. Find the Ballet Award, the Tap Award, Lily and Eddie.

3 feather headbands

4 ballet bags

5 purple waistcoats

6 tutus

7 leg warmers

8 tiaras

9 butterfly clips

10 bow ties

12 pink rosettes

15 dancing hamsters

STUNNING SINGERS

Miss Harmony has been working hard to get everyone ready for the opera round. Can you find Lily, Eddie and the Opera Singing Award?

3 harp players

6 necklaces

9 Roman headdresses

10 leaf fans

15 feathers

THE BIG
THEATRE CHALLENGE

CRAZY CIRCUS

Roll up, roll up! In round nine, the pupils need to amaze the judges with their incredible circus skills. Spot Lily, Eddie and the Circus Skills Award.

3 unicycles

6 clown shoes

9 circus toys

10 joke flowers

15 juggling clubs

MAGICAL MUSICALS

The all-singing, all-dancing musical theatre round is the last one before the final show. Can you see Lily, Eddie and the Musical Theatre Award?

3 electric guitars

4 disco lights

5 leather jackets

6 wigs

7 fairy wings

8 microphone stands

9 red shoes

10 fairy wands

12 pairs of sunglasses

15 hedgehogs

MAKE-UP MAYHEM

The students have won their place in the final. It's time to get ready, starting with make-up. There's no award to look for, but can you find Lily and Eddie?

3 make-up artists

6 mirrors

9 hairbrushes

10 lipsticks

15 make-up brushes

BUSY BACKSTAGE

The show is about to start. See if you can spot Lily and Eddie as they wait nervously backstage. Will everyone be ready in time for the final show?

2 pairs of trainers

6 pineapples

9 boxes of chocolates

10 T-shirts

15 donuts

FANTASTIC FINAL

Everyone's trying their best, hoping to become the Big Theatre Challenge champions. Spot Lily, Eddie and the special, silver Best Stage School award.

 1 director

4 pink stars

5 walkie-talkies

 6 squirrels

7 ice creams

8 red sweatbands

9 squeaking mice

10 microphones

13 show programmes

15 show tickets

PERFECT PARTY

And the winner is... Superstar Stage School! It's time for a big party to celebrate. Can you see Lily, Eddie and the silver Best Stage School award?

3 large pizzas

4 disco balls

5 camera phones

6 fizzy drinks

7 platform shoes

8 funky spotlights

9 party poppers

10 balloons

12 cupcakes

15 party hats

Well done! You've helped Superstar Stage School win the Big Theatre Challenge. Now go back and look at every scene again. Can you find these characters and items on every page?

Mr Disco

The Big Theatre Challenge poster

Miss Harmony

Melody the parrot

Dani the dancing cat

Mr Tap

Jazz the musical dog

Neon boom box

How closely were you looking? Go back and see if you can find which page each of these is hidden on.

A dancer in a robot costume

A singer in a Roman helmet

An actor with a false beard

A rabbit with a flower